THE BEANO

BOOK 1974

Bursting onto comic stands in December 1937, The Dandy was
filled to the brim with hilarious tales and quirky characters.
With readers hungry for more, they were introduced to the
cast of Beano in July 1938. These two titles became beloved by
children and adults alike across Britain, and it quickly became
evident that the classic characters from the pages of Beano and
The Dandy had an appetite for comedy.

From plots and pranks to ingenious inventions and sticky
situations, food has often served as a catalyst for capers in
Beano and The Dandy. Readers from across the nation have
been introduced to Dandy delicacies, such as Desperate Dan's
favourite cow pie, and have witnessed clever tricks by Britain's
most famous menaces and minxes in order to get their hands on
their favourite sweet treats!

This classic collection presents a feast of the best strips from
the past eight decades, specially selected from DC Thomson's
archives. Putting the heavy-hitting casts of these two titles
head-to- head, these strips will find out who the cleverest,
greediest, messiest, and funniest food-loving favourites are in
this ultimate comic FOOD FIGHT!

© DCT Consumer Products (UK) Ltd 2018
D.C. Thomson and Co. Ltd,
185 Fleet Street,
London EC4A 2HS

Printed in China

Much of the humour in Beano and The Dandy stems from cartooning during the Second World War.
Throughout the 1940s, our favourite characters made the most of helping their fellow soldiers, and their hearty appetite
for hilarity developed through Britain's rationing restrictions.

THE DANDY COMIC

Nº 129 - MAY 18th 1940
EVERY FRIDAY
2D

KORKY THE CAT

OUR KORKY NOW IS ARMY COOK.
SOME PRIVATES PINCH HIS DUFF —
WITH POTS AND PANS HE PAYS THEM BACK,
AND THE COLONEL CUTS UP ROUGH!

TA-RA-RA
TA-RA-RA
TA-RA-TARA-TARA-RA

OW! WHO D'YOU THINK YOU'RE SHOVING?

HERE ARE OUR GUNS AND HELMETS!

GOSH! SOMEONE'S NAILED DOWN THE BLACK-OUT BLINDS AND THE LIGHT'S BUST!

WHY ON EARTH DID THEY SOUND THE BUGLE TO FALL IN FOR PARADE AT THIS TIME?

THE BEANO COMIC

No. 232—MAY 20th, 1944　2ᴰ

HUNGRY HORACE

HUNGRY HORACE

HUNGRY HORACE

Calamitous cooking could be used to the characters' advantage, as Pansy Potter demonstrated in 1940.
But, for others, it often landed them in trouble, as shown in this Rip Van Wink comic from 1942.

Nº 111 · JAN. 13TH · 1940
EVERY FRIDAY
2ᴰ

THE DANDY COMIC

KORKY THE CAT

KORKY'S STUNT FOR CUTTING BREAD
MAKES AN AIRMAN SURE SEE RED.
HE TRIES TO GET HIS OWN BACK—BUT
KORKY MAKES HIM LOOK A MUTT!

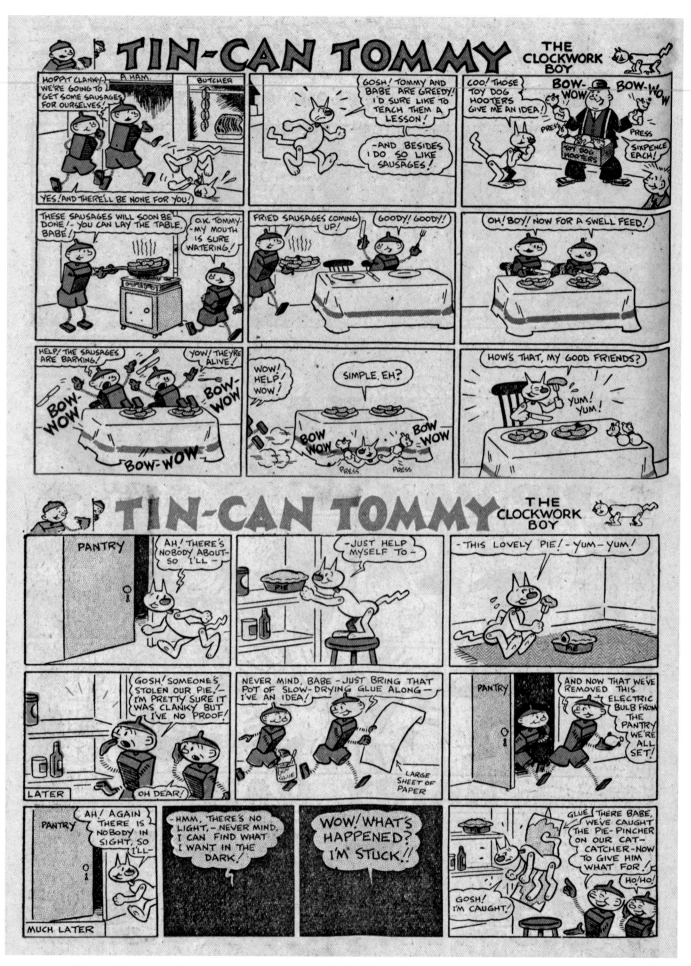

Through the years, these characters have used their skills and smarts to best their friends and foes.
Their quick thinking usually led to them being rewarded with a fantastic feast.
Those driven by greed, however, often ended with their clever plans backfiring!

PLUM MacDUFF
THE HIGHLANDMAN WHO NEVER GETS ENOUGH

PLUM MacDUFF
THE HIGHLANDMAN WHO NEVER GETS ENOUGH

PLUM MacDUFF
THE HIGHLANDMAN WHO NEVER GETS ENOUGH

LAZY JONES

LAZY JONES

L. J. really is no dope – he's good with his spaghetti rope.

ROGER the DODGER

DESPERATE DAN

LORD SNOOTY AND HIS PALS

Korky has long been pestered by the family of mice living in his home. In this hilarious strip from 1953, he finally found a solution to his pesky problem.

THE BEANO COMIC

No. 316—AUG. 23rd, 1947   2ᴰ

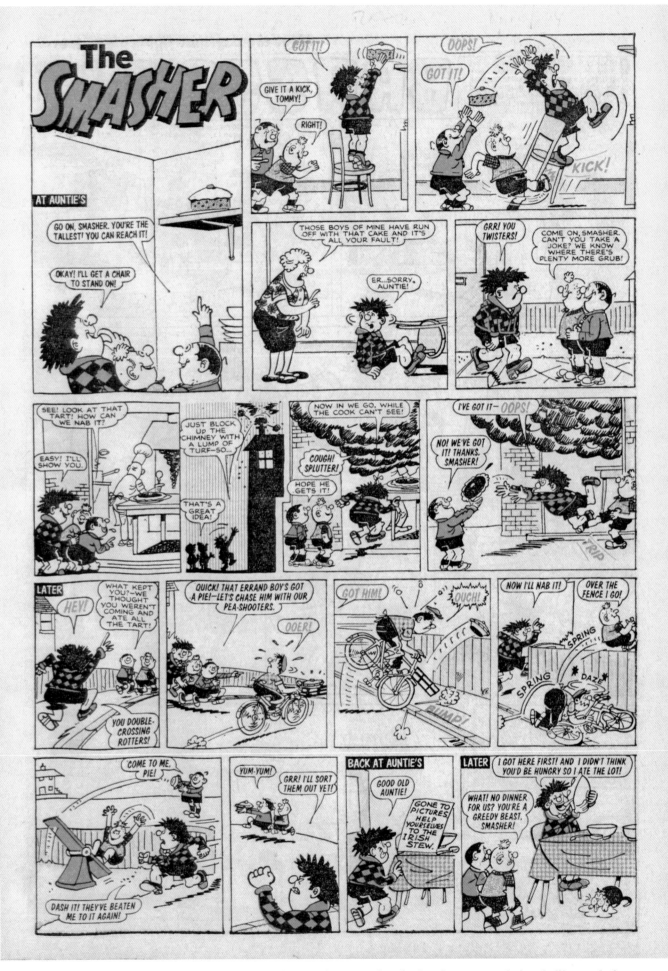

Occasionally, family members have managed to get the upper hand when it comes to their rebellious relatives,
but in this strip from 1966, Smasher ultimately wins the day – and the stew.

The queerest plants you'll ever see—A jam tart bush and a pudding tree!

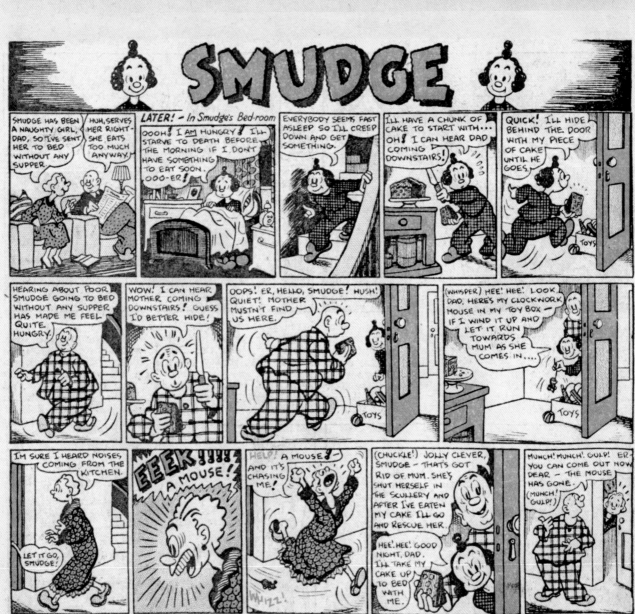

THE BEANO

PUTS BIG SMILES ON LITTLE FACES!

No. 940—July 23rd, 1960.

2ᴰ

EVERY THURSDAY

BIFFO THE BEAR

BEWARE OF FIERCE DOG

~AND I'VE GOT TO DELIVER MEAT HERE!

THIS DOG DOESN'T LOOK FIERCE! IT'S OPENING THE GATE FOR ME~

~USHERING ME IN~

~AND LICKING MY HAND. THAT NOTICE IS NONSENSE!

LICK!

NOW IT'S RINGING THE BELL FOR ME!

RING!

PRESS

YOUR MEAT, MA'AM. NICE DOG YOU HAVE!

PRESS

BUT, OUT IN THE STREET AGAIN...

WHO'S PINCHED MY SAUSAGES?

BEWARE OF FIERCE DOG

BEWARE OF FIERCE DOG

MUNCH! MUNCH!

BEWARE OF ~~FIERCE~~ FRIENDLY DOG

SLURP!

THAT'S MORE LIKE IT, YOU CRAFTY HOUND!

The comic cast of Beano and The Dandy have never been fans of minding their manners! In hilarious strips full of sloshing, splashing and slurping, our favourite characters have always laughed in the face of fine dining etiquette, despite the best efforts of their disgruntled parents and relatives. In this classic Minnie the Minx strip from 1963, we see Dad's solution to Minnie's beastly habits!

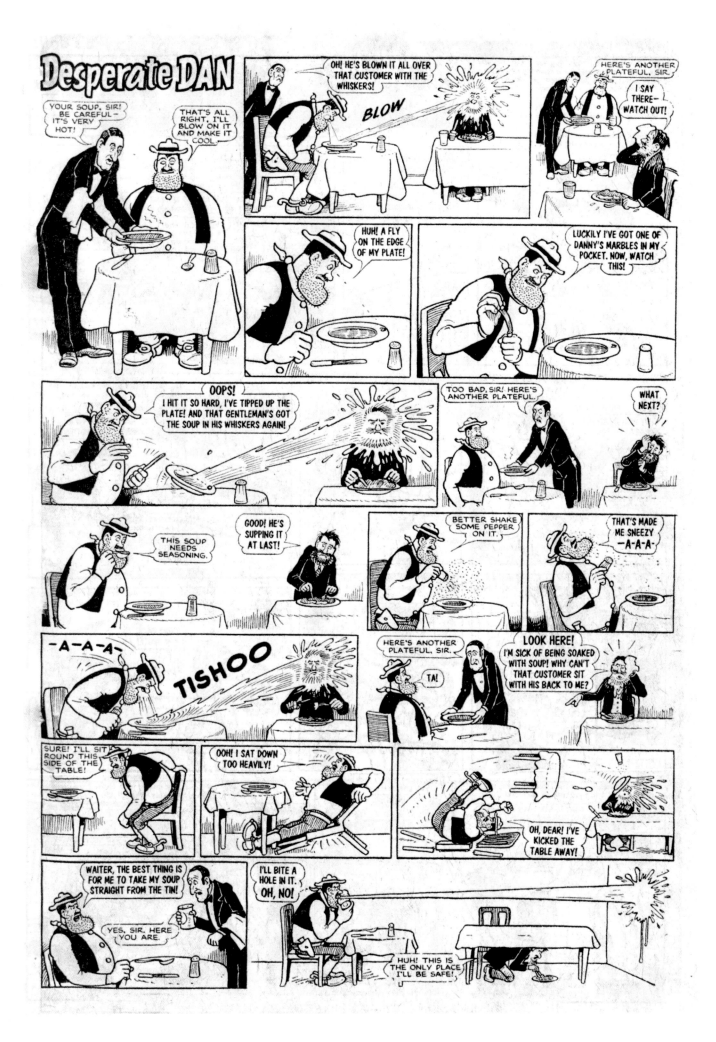

CHARLEY BRAND fairly whistled with envy when he spotted his Dad at the dining room window of the Hotel Posh. Dad Brand was entertaining one of his boss's business friends, and both Charley and his amazing metal pal, Brassneck, reckoned he must be having the time of his life. They were both dead wrong!

GOSH! DAD'S A LUCKY DUFFER HAVING A MEAL IN THERE. IT MUST BE COSTING HIM A FORTUNE.

LOOK! HE'S WAVING TO US, CHARLEY!

Dad Brand was in a cold sweat! He was trying to signal Charley to tell him that he'd forgotten his wallet and didn't have any cash to pay the hotel bill!

ER—HAVE ANOTHER CUP OF TEA, MR CROCKETT?

NO, THANK YOU.

WHAT IMPUDENCE BRAND HAS! ASKING ME FOR MONEY!

HO-HO! HE'S IN A FIX NOW!

In desperation, poor Dad had even tried to borrow money from Prof. Watt who was dining nearby with Mrs Watt and their son Swotty. But the Prof was no friend of Mr Brand.

There would be big trouble if the businessman was made to wash dishes and Dad knew his desperate plan had to work.

PSSST! FIND CHARLEY BRAND AND GIVE HIM THIS NOTE, SONNY. QUICK AS YOU CAN!

OKAY, MISTER.

The lad did his job. Dad beamed when he heard Charley's call at the door.

OVER HERE, DAD. I'VE SOMETHING FOR YOU.

PHEW! WHAT A RELIEF!

Swotty Watt was enjoying watching Dad suffer, however, and he switched on a radio box which he carried.

This gadget gave Swotty control over Brassneck, and at once a strange gleam came into the metal lad's eye.

OUT OF MY WAY, BOY!

WHAT'S THIS YOU'VE GOT? NOODLES!

In a flash the metal maddie grabbed all those noodles and began to dish them out around the room. There would be oodles of trouble over this!

BLOOP! HERE'S A NOODLE WIG FOR YOU, MISSUS! HAW-HAW!

SHRIEK!

WOW!

EEK! MY NOODLES! COME BACK!

Sure enough, Brassneck's noodle nonsense got him and Charley booted out of the hotel just as Swotty had planned.

OUT, YOU HOOLIGANS!

OH, NO!

YOU SILLY MUTT, BRASSNECK!

Charley had a plan to get the wallet delivered to Dad's table, and it might have worked if Swotty hadn't overheard and switched on his gadget again.

HEE-HEE! I'LL SOON SCUTTLE BRAND'S SCHEME.

BLEEP! GIVE ME THAT WALLET OR I'LL FLATTEN YOU, BRAND.

HEY!

Poor Charley was furious when Brassneck waded off through the hotel pond with the wallet.

COME BACK, YOU METAL TRAITOR! WHAT'S GOT INTO YOU?

BLEEP! WATCH ME PLAY ANOTHER TRICK!

What was the metal clown up to? Before anyone could stop him, he sneaked into the hotel kitchen.

APRIL IN PARIS TUM-TI-TI-TUM-TUM!

HEE-HEE! QUIETLY DOES IT, BLOOP!

What a surprise for Dad when a brass waiter suddenly showed up at his table.

SOMETHING SPECIALLY FOR YOU, MR BRAND.

I BET I CAN GUESS WHAT'S IN THERE. WELL DONE, BRASSY!

A big surprise too when the brass waiter lifted the cover off the dish and out popped a frog, fresh from the hotel pond!

HAW-HAW! WHAT A JOKE!

EEK! A FROG!

Dad felt badly let down, and now the manager eyed him suspiciously.

YAIEE! IT'S ALL GREEN AND SLIMY!

CATCH EET!

YOUR BILL, SIR?

ER—NOT YET! I'LL HAVE ANOTHER CUP OF TEA.

The Dandy and Beano characters have often been tempted by tasty treats.
Very few are able to resist their cravings.

SMARTY GRANDPA

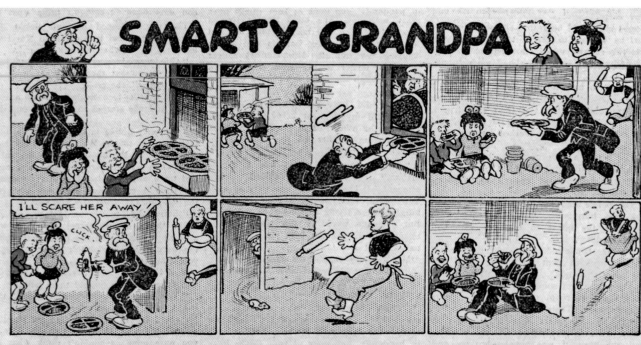

SMARTY GRANDPA

SMARTY GRANDPA

FREDDY FLIPPER-FEET

WHEN THE BELL RINGS!

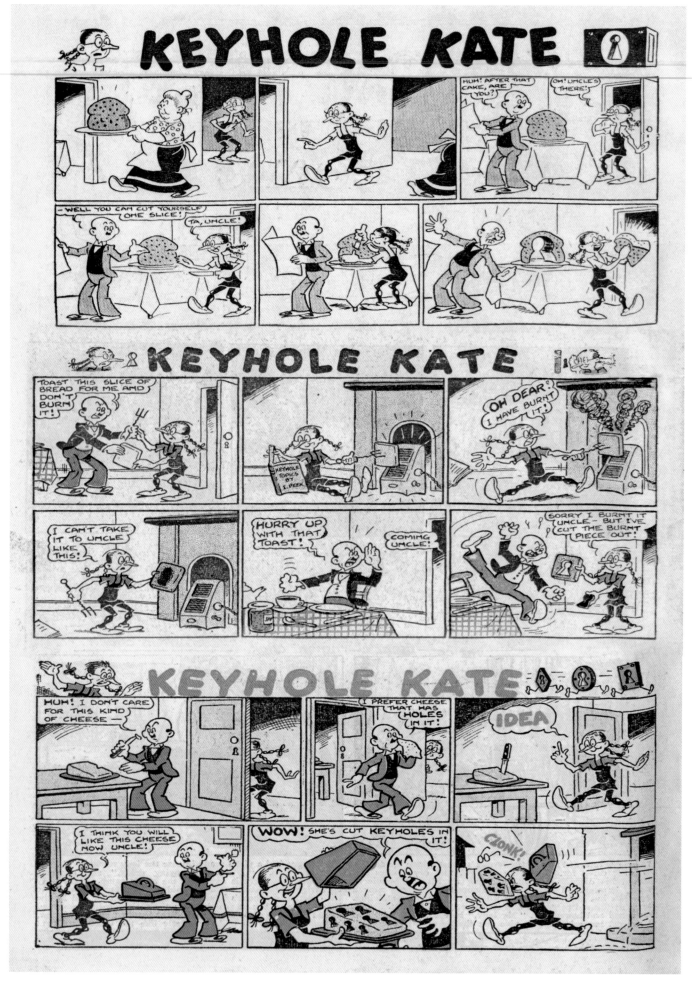

One of The Dandy's nosiest characters, Keyhole Kate, can find keyholes in anything – even food!

IN COOKERY CLASS—

YOU CAN MAKE ANY-THING YOU LIKE TODAY, GIRLS.

OH, BOY!

SO—

I'LL MAKE MY FAVOURITE FOOD!

THEN—

I'M SUPER AT MAKING PANCAKES. HUP!

BUT—

HEY! IT SHOULD HAVE COME DOWN BY NOW!

OH, DEAR!

ENTER HEADMISTRESS—

THERE'S TO BE A COOKING COMPETITION—COOK YOUR ENTRIES TONIGHT AND...

LATER—

THAT WILL BE ALL, GIRLS!

PLOP!

THAT NIGHT—

I THINK I'LL MAKE PANCAKES FOR THE COMPETITION.

SELF RAISING FLOUR

SO—

TEE-TUM! RUMPY, PUM!

THEN—

OH, NO! THEY'RE SPOILED—AND IT'S TOO LATE TO MAKE ANY MORE!

The Beano

3D

EVERY THURSDAY
No. 1302—July 1st, 1967

Grockle's Not Feeling so Good, Poor Lad—Give Him an Apple, or He'll Go Mad!

JIMMY AND HIS GROCKLE

1—Grockle is Jimmy Johnson's queer-looking pet. He looks like a dragon, but he's far tougher than the toughest dragon that ever breathed fire and flames. Just now, however, he was nearly in tears.

2—For he wanted a toffee apple, and couldn't get one because they cost a penny each. And Grockle was broke! As for Jimmy, he only had a lump of well-chewed gum and a length of string in his pockets.

3—So Grockle had to do without his toffee apple—but he didn't forget about it! When Jimmy joined in a game of football his queer-looking pet was still thinking of juicy toffee apples, and so he pinched the ball.

4—It looked like an apple, but Grockle soon found out the difference when he tried to eat it. However, he thought the ball might be an egg, so he built a big nest in a tree and tried to hatch the "egg" out!

5—The ball hatched out quicker than Grockle expected. At least it burst its skin when Jimmy's baby dragon shoved his sharp-pointed tail into it. Grockle nearly jumped out of his skin with fright!

6—Grockle marched off with a face longer than a giraffe's neck. But his ugly mug soon creased into a huge grin. In fact the grin was so huge that it nearly split the back of his neck. What had he seen?

7—It was a box of eggs outside Grumpy the Grocer's shop door! Grockle tried to hatch them out, but not one of the eggs stood up to his weight. They smashed!

8—Grockle was peeved—but the shop-keeper was more peeved. In fact, he was jumping mad. He chased after Jimmy's pet, but Grockle soon left him behind.

9—He saw a boy passing with a basket of eggs and on these he breathed his fiery breath. At once the eggshells broke, and out popped hordes of tiny, wee chickens!

10—Grockle was so proud that he gave a dance of joy. Then right away, he marched the chickens along to the toffee apple shop where he tried to exchange them for a couple of juicy toffee apples.

11—But there was nothing doing. Then Grockle spied a tub of toffee for coating the apples. While he eyed it longingly, Jimmy gave a junk man the chickens for a load of boxing gloves and other junk.

12—With the junk Grockle and he made toffee apples — but what apples! The lads they gave them to, licked off the toffee and played football with the " apples." Grockle, however, ate the apples as well.

Dennis the Menace's faithful dog, Gnasher, is renowned for his love of sausages. In this gnawesome strip from 1969, the origin story of the trusty dog and his favourite food is revealed for the first time.

Cow pie has been a staple of Desperate Dan's diet since he first appeared in The Dandy. Over the years, his appetite for them has only grown, and the massive main course has become as recognisable as the strongman himself.

No. 255—DEC. 11th, 1943

THE DANDY COMIC

2D

KORKY THE CAT

WITH POSTER, CLOTH AND BOX,
KORKY CUNNING AS A FOX,
FAKES UP A POSH MEAL —
TO SELL TO GREEDY P.C. HEEL!

THE Nibblers

The cast of Beano and The Dandy have regularly risen to the challenge of baking. More often than not, they succeeded in creating chaos rather than cakes!

PA'S HAVING HIS AFTER-DINNER NAP AND GUESS WHAT HE'S DREAMING ABOUT.

SWEET DREAMS

WHY, HIS TEA, OF COURSE!

YUM-YUM! WE'LL HAVE HIGH TEA TONIGHT. FIRST, CHICKEN SOUP—

—FOLLOWED BY ROAST-BEEF, YORKSHIRE PUD, MASHED POTATOES, PEAS AND GRAVY—

—AND ROUNDED OFF WITH ICE-CREAM, TRIFLE, JELLY AND DUMPLING. SLURP!

TEA-TIME— WELL, MA, WHERE'S THE CHICKEN SOUP, ROAST BEEF, ICE-CREAM, TRIFLE, JELLY AND DUMPLING?

WHAT ARE YOU RAVING ABOUT, PA?—

—YOU KNOW WE ALWAYS HAVE HASH ON THURSDAYS.

UGH! WHAT AN INSULT TO A GREAT EATER LIKE ME!

WELL, PA, IF YOU'RE NOT PLEASED, WHY DON'T *YOU* DO THE COOKING?

SO— I SHALL PREPARE A FEAST FIT FOR A KING.

WE'RE OFF FOR A STROLL TO WORK UP AN APPETITE.

FLOUR

TUM-TEE-TUM! SOON BE READY NOW.

CACKLE! I'LL SNAFFLE THAT LOT!

COME BACK WITH THAT GRUB, YOU THIEVING VULTURE!

WOW! BUILDER BOOM!

QUICK! TURN OFF THAT CEMENT MIXER!

GROAN! TOO LATE! CAN I BORROW THIS MACHINE FOR A BIT?

SURE, PA.

WELL, WHERE'S THE GREAT MEAL?

YES, WHERE?

ER!—IT'LL HAVE TO BE HASH AS USUAL ON THURSDAYS/GULP!

BAH! TRUST PA TO MAKE A HASH OF THINGS!

THE BASH STREET KIDS

THE star wangler of Greytowers School was fed up, and the reason was plain. The reason was the food—which was also very plain. The same old thing day after day, week after week. No wonder Winker made up his mind to do something about it.

As Winker left the dining hall, he heard a snatch of conversation between the Head and his Form Master, Mr Creep.

Winker Watson, the super-spy had a plan on the boil!

The plan was to swipe the Head's menu and put in its place the slap-up one Winker had prepared himself!

But a terrific surprise awaited the wangler.

Suddenly—footsteps! There was no time to get back out the window. Winker plunged into hiding.

Miss Creep was Creepy's sister and Headmistress of Oak Lodge Girls' School next door. While they schemed together, Winker listened.

So it needed an inspector's visit to make the Head buck up his ideas! Well, Winker would give the inspector plenty to report!

Winker needed the help of the Oak Lodge girls, but they were always willing!

Cookie was dead chuffed by all the pleas for advice. He didn't dream that he was about to walk into a trap!

A food inspector gets a shock — With soup that tastes of soap and chalk!

WHACKO! THE GIRLS ARE GETTING COOKIE OUT OF THE COOKHOUSE! IN WE GO, TROTTY!

YOU FLATTER ME, GIRLS, AND I'LL BE ONLY TOO HAPPY TO COME AND GIVE YOU SOME EXPERT ADVICE!

JOLLY DECENT OF YOU, COOKIE!

But Cookie wouldn't have been so pleased had he seen Winker and Trotty lurking there and known what they had in that sack!

NEXT DAY The school meals inspector arrived just before lunch, and was greeted by the Head.

WELCOME TO GREYTOWERS, INSPECTOR! WE'LL HAVE LUNCH FIRST, AND AFTERWARDS YOU CAN EXAMINE THE KITCHEN.

I'M ON SERVING DUTY TODAY, MR CREEP, SIR!

RIGHT, TROTT! GET READY TO SERVE SOUP TO THE INSPECTOR FIRST.

DINING HALL ←

The inspector's soup! Fancy letting Winker's closest pal get within a mile of it!

I'LL ADD A SPOT OF FLAVOURING TO THE INSPECTOR'S SOUP BEFORE I TAKE IT IN.

KITCH RULES MEAL TIMES

SOAP POWDER *SUGAR*

Oh, boy! This would get the inspector into a lather—or a lather into the inspector!

One spoonful was enough for the horrified visitor.

UGH!, GROOGH! DO YOU CALL THIS REVOLTING STUFF SOUP, HEADMASTER? *SPLUTTER!*

YOU DON'T LIKE IT, INSPECTOR?

GRR! I'VE DECIDED I'M NOT HUNGRY, HEADMASTER, AND IF YOU'LL LEAD THE WAY I'D LIKE TO INSPECT THE KITCHEN!

Y-YES, INSPECTOR!

DINING HALL ←

By now the Head was worried. When the inspector disliked the soup that much, what fault would he pick with the kitchen?

PSST! THE HEAD'S ON HIS WAY, COOKIE, AND HE WANTS YOU TO PUT ON THIS CLEAN APRON TO IMPRESS THE INSPECTOR.

RIGHT, YOUNG WATSON, THANKS!

Watch it, Cookie! There's a dark plot afoot!

WHY, YOU YOUNG SCOUNDREL, WATSON—IT'S FULL OF SOOT!

HEE HEE!

Oh, dear! And there wasn't time to clean up now, either!

The inspector was shocked to meet such a dirty-looking school cook. He sniffed around suspiciously.

BAH! DISGRACEFUL, HEADMASTER! I ONLY HOPE THE OVEN IS CLEANER THAN YOUR COOK.

I'LL TALK TO YOU LATER, COOK!

EEEK! MATRON'S CAT! JUST WAIT TILL I SEE CREEP!

S-SPIT!

What a faceful the inspector got! A face full of scratches!

THANK YOU, MISS CREEP! IT'S A PITY THEY DON'T SERVE MEALS LIKE THIS AT YOUR BROTHER'S SCHOOL!

DON'T MENTION IT, INSPECTOR!

RIGHT, WINKER. YOUR GRUB COMING UP NEXT!

MR CREEP! I DEMAND AN EXPLANATION!

The inspector wouldn't allow the boys to eat in Greytowers, so they all trooped across to Oak Lodge for a super slap-up lunch. Mealtimes would be a bit brighter in Greytowers after the inspector made his report.

BILLY WHIZZ

DESPERATE DAN

Diabolical chef, and general jinx, Jonah regularly found himself in trouble with his cooking attempts, despite his best efforts.

WILLIE WOODPECKER

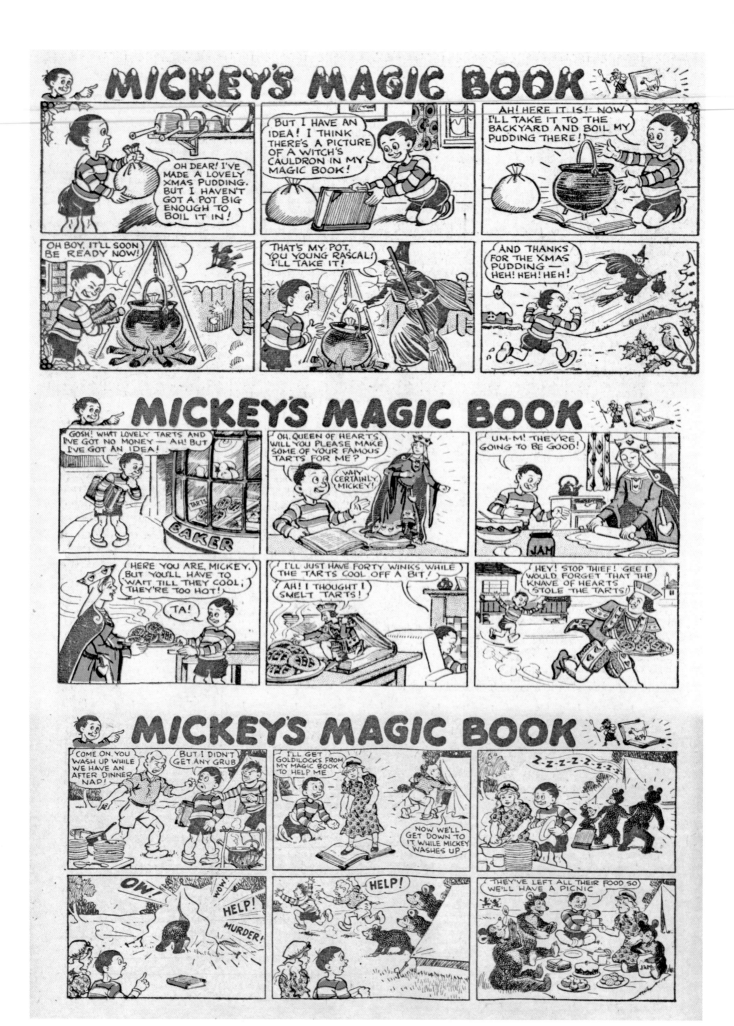

Mickey's Magic Book had a habit of cooking up trouble for the young boy.

PANSY POTTER
IN WONDERLAND

THE THREE BEARS

Although the cast of Beano and The Dandy adore their food, one thing has always given them trouble – vegetables.
In this classic dodge from 1966, Roger's attempt to be rid of Mum's cabbages doesn't quite go as planned.

CHARLIE CHUTNEY THE COMICAL COOK

CHARLIE CHUTNEY THE COMICAL COOK

CHARLIE CHUTNEY THE COMICAL COOK

The Beano

EVERY THURSDAY

No. 1293—APR. 29th, 1967.

3D-

DESPERATE DAN

PANSY POTTER THE STRONG MAN'S DAUGHTER

GREAT NEW THRILL PICTURES INSIDE — IN TURTLE BOY

THE DANDY

2ᴰ

EVERY TUESDAY

No. 761—JUNE 23rd, 1956.

KORKY the CAT

KORKY'S DOWN AND "OUT" TODAY. HE SURE IS FEELING GLUM, AND ALL BECAUSE HIS HEAD GOT WHAT WAS MEANT TO GO IN HIS TUM!

Terrible table manners can mean eating in cafes and restaurants is a rare experience for our comic characters. Eating out regularly ended in embarrassment for bewildered parents and outraged onlookers. Sometimes it was safer to bring the fine-dining experience home instead.

The children in Beano and The Dandy dreaded school dinners. Over the years, they have attempted a number of dodges, plans, and wangles in an effort to avoid gruesome grub from the dinner hall.

WINKER WATSON

OH, NO! IT'S CORNED BEEF AGAIN, WINKER!

YOU'RE RIGHT, TROTTY! AND WE'VE HAD IT FOR EVERY MEAL THIS WEEK!

THE boys of Greytowers School were fed up with their food—and no wonder. They had got the same thing for dinner, tea and supper for days on end. Winker Watson, the school's star wangler, felt he'd grow horns if he ate any more bully beef!

SORRY, LADS IT'S NOT MY DOING! MR CREEP GOT A BARGAIN OF A DOZEN LARGE TINS OF BULLY BEEF AND HE'S TOLD ME TO USE IT UP.

CHUCK AWAY YOUR TIN OPENER COOKIE!

FED UP WITH BULLY BEEF!

CORNED BEEF IS CORNY!

KITCHEN OUT of BOUNDS

The demonstration outside the cookhouse was to no avail. Cookie's hands were tied.

But Winker Watson's brain wasn't tied, and the wangler soon thought out a scheme.

IT'S NOT POOR OLD COOKIE'S FAULT, LADS, SO WE'LL HAVE TO DO SOMETHING ABOUT IT OURSELVES. HERE'S WHAT WE'LL TRY...

LET'S HOPE YOUR PLAN WORKS, WINKER!

JOLLY SPORTING OF MY THIRD FORMERS TO OFFER TO CUT YOUR PRIVATE LAWN, EH, HEADMASTER?

RATHER, MR CREEP, AND THEY'RE MAKING A NICE JOB OF IT TOO!

CARRY ON MOWING, LADS, WHILE TROTTY AND I DUMP ANOTHER BARROWLOAD OF CUTTINGS!

The Head and Mr Creep, the boys' Form Master, should have smelt a rat right away. Imagine Winker and his pals actually volunteering to work!

This was the explanation. It was all a ruse to get rid of the corned beef!

THIS IS THE LAST TIN OF BULLY LEFT, TROTTY— HIDE IT IN THE BARROW, AND DUMP IT WITH THE OTHERS!

NO. ONE WILL EVER FIND THEM HIDDEN IN THE WOODS, WINKER.

KITC OUT o

LATER- CREEPY AND HIS SISTER AGNES TAKE A STROLL...

—and Creepy was remembering the days of long ago!

...YOU KNOW, I USED TO LOVE KICKING NEWLY-CUT GRASS ABOUT WHEN I WAS YOUNG...

YEE-OWL!

Creepy didn't half get a shock when he kicked that "nice soft heap" of cut grass!

WHOOSH!

Those tins were packed with solid goodness—but they didn't do Creepy's skull any good at all!

CLARENCE.!!

BONK!

OO! MY TOE! MY HEAD!

But see how his crafty plans end in an "eggs"traordinary event!

Of course, Creepy guessed who had transported the tins, and he gave Winker and Trotty a real telling off.

WATSON! TROTT! YOU'LL SUFFER FOR THIS! FROM NOW ON, I'LL KEEP THE CORNED BEEF IN MY STUDY, AND I'LL DEAL WITH YOU LATER!

YESSIR, MR CREEP SIR!

Winker wasn't discouraged, however. He made a deal with the girls of Oak Lodge School next door.

...THAT'S A GREAT IDEA, WINKER. WE NEVER GET BULLY BEEF, SO WE'LL RAID OUR PANTRY AND SWOP YOU OTHER GRUB FOR IT.

RIGHT, GIRLS, AND HERE'S WHAT TO DO TO HELP US GET OUR HANDS ON THE BULLY BEEF!

The girls were always keen to help Winker with a wangle, and they used a bit of flattery on Creepy.

GOOD! THE GIRLS HAVE GOT CREEPY OUT OF HIS ROOM—WE'LL SNEAK IN AS SOON AS HE'S OUT OF SIGHT!

RIGHT, WINKER!

Winker and Trotty sneaked off to hide the bully beef once again.

QUICK! WE'LL HIDE IT IN THE DORM FOR NOW, TROTTY!

5 MINUTES LATER ~

I'VE BEEN ROBBED! SEARCH EVERY ROOM UNTIL MY TINS ARE FOUND!

HEY, THAT'S CREEPY'S VOICE! QUICK, LET'S GET THE STUFF OUT OF HERE BEFORE HE COMES SNOOPING ROUND!

Creepy must have returned sooner than expected. His roar of rage could have been heard a mile away!

The pals escaped from the furious Creepy by a whisker!

PHEW! MADE IT—BUT WE'D BETTER SLING THEM OVER THE WALL IN CASE WE'RE CAUGHT!

HEAVE! OVER THEY GO...GOSH, WHAT WAS THAT?

CRASH! SPLAT! CRUNCH!

But there was a shock for Winker and Trotty when they tossed the tins over the wall into the Oak Lodge grounds.

OO-ER! THEY LANDED SLAP-BANG IN THE BOX THE GIRLS HAD READY FOR US! WATCH IT, SOMEBODY'S COMING!

Oh, no! What a pity the girls had chosen that very spot to lay down the box of grub for Winker!

It was Miss Creep, the Head of the girls' school who arrived first, but Creepy, who was her brother, wasn't far behind.

EEEK! WHO DID THAT, CLARENCE? ALL MY LOVELY EGGS—SMASHED!

I DON'T KNOW, AGNES, BUT GIVE ME BACK MY TINS OF CORNED BEEF!

Miss Creep knew a bargain when she saw one, and since it was Creepy's bully beef that had done the damage, the bully beef could pay for it!

NOT LIKELY, CLARENCE! I'M KEEPING THEM, AND YOU CAN HAVE ALL THOSE DOZENS OF BROKEN EGGS, AND IT JOLLY WELL SERVES YOU RIGHT.

And so, after all that effort, the lads were even worse off than before! For once, Winker Watson, the wiliest wangler of them all, had made a great big boob!

OH, NO! SCRAMBLED EGGS AGAIN, WINKER— THAT'S EVERY DAY THIS WEEK!

UGH!

SORRY, LADS, AND IT'S ALL MY FAULT! IT'S THE LAST TIME I'LL EVER BEEF ABOUT BULLY AGAIN!

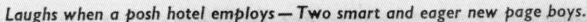

Charley gets the supper he wishes—While Dad washes stacks and stacks of dishes?

Dad Brand's heart missed a beat when he heard the manager rap out an order.

NOW MOVE THAT HAT STAND INTO A CORNER!

In the nick of time, Dad dived under a nearby table to avoid being seen by Brassneck.

SHOULD MANAGE THIS JOB WITHOUT ANY BOOBS!

This was Dad's chance to get Brassneck sacked! He stuck out his foot in the metal boy's path.

OOF!

WOW!

But the chums escaped with a severe telling off.

YOU TWO ARE ON YOUR LAST CHANCE! NOW GET AWAY TO THE KITCHEN!

Before Dad could scramble out from under the table, the head waiter arrived with two guests, Mr and Mrs Plunkett.

THIS WAY, MADAM!

As she sat down, Mrs Plunkett's sharp-pointed heel jabbed Dad in the rear end.

With a squeal of pain, Mr Brand went straight up in the air, carrying the table with him!

AARGH!

HELP! THERE'S A WILD BEAST UNDER THIS TABLE!

WOW!

Dad had to do some rapid thinking to explain things to the manager.

YOU RUFFIAN! WHAT WERE YOU DOING UNDER THAT TABLE?

ER—I DROPPED A CUFF-LINK AND I WAS LOOKING FOR IT ON THE FLOOR!

Dad couldn't run any more risks. He must get away from the hotel before the chums spotted him.

BAH! HERE'S CHARLEY NOW, AND I HAVEN'T EVEN BEEN ABLE TO FINISH MY SOUP COURSE!

More bad luck for Dad! As he crept along on hands and knees, one of the waiters tripped over him and his tray of dishes went flying.

OOPS!

LOOK OUT, THERE!

There would have been a tremendous smash—but for Brassneck. The metal marvel threw himself forward and caught the lot!

WELL SAVED, BOY! BUT WHAT'S GOING ON HERE?

Dad was nabbed. His game was up and now he was in bigger trouble than ever.

SO! TRYING TO CREEP OUT WITHOUT PAYING YOUR BILL, ARE YOU?

Charley and Brassneck were in the manager's good books because of that wonder save. The chums sat down to a slap-up feed in the kitchen and Charley got his fish and chips. Dad was not so lucky. He had to wash mountains of dishes —but it served him right!

HOPE THE BOYS DON'T RECOGNISE ME!

EAT UP, LADS!

24-2-68

THE END

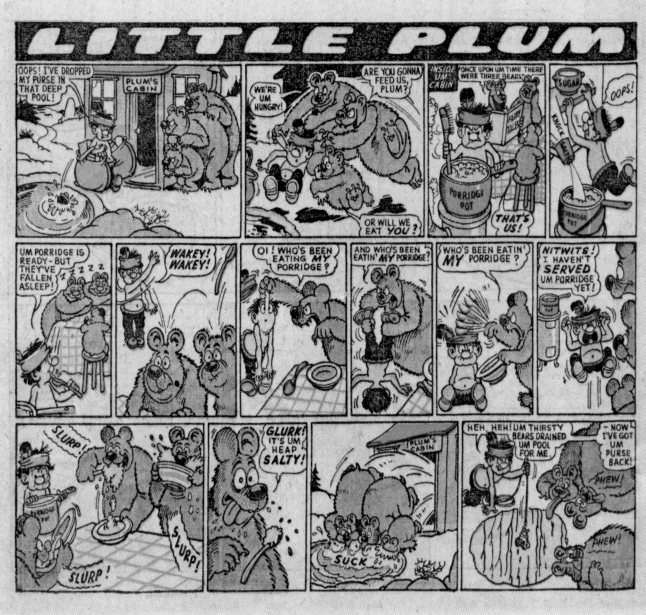

MINNIE THE MINX

I'M LOOKING FORWARD TO THIS, READERS. I'M STARVING!

I SAY, WAITER!

TEN MINUTES LATER—

WAITER!

GRR! I'M FED UP WITH THIS!

EEK!

HEH! HEH!

ER—STEAK PIE FOR ME, PLEASE.

GRR!

SO—

SUPER!

LATER—

THAT WAS NICE!

YES, LET'S GET OUR BILL!

WAITER!

LATER—

I SAY, WAITER!

I'LL SOON ATTRACT HIS ATTENTION, DAD!

NO! STOP!

AW! TOO LATE!

HAR! HAR! BULL'S EYE!

YOUR BILL, SIR! SNARL!

ER—GULP! THANK YOU!

NEXT DAY—

WE CAN GET A GOOD MEAL JUST ROUND THE CORNER.

OH, BOY! IS IT ANOTHER RESTAURANT, DAD?

NO—THIS IS THE ONLY PLACE YOUR MANNERS ARE FIT FOR!

JOE'S HOT

TRY OU DELICIOU HOT DOGS

HUH!

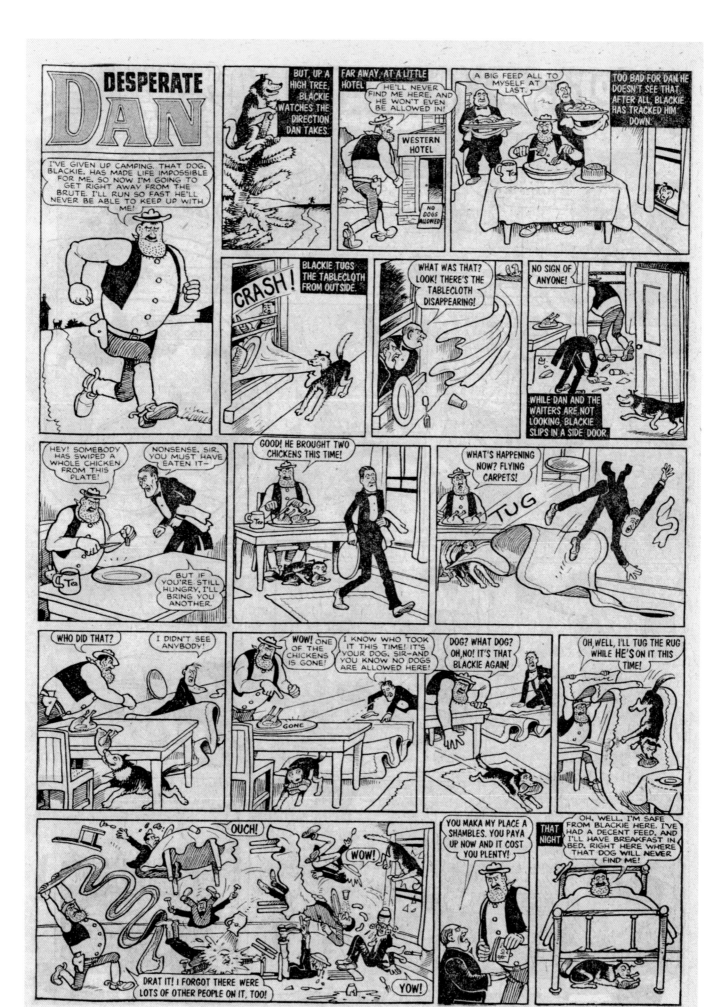

THE TRICKS OF SCREWY DRIVER

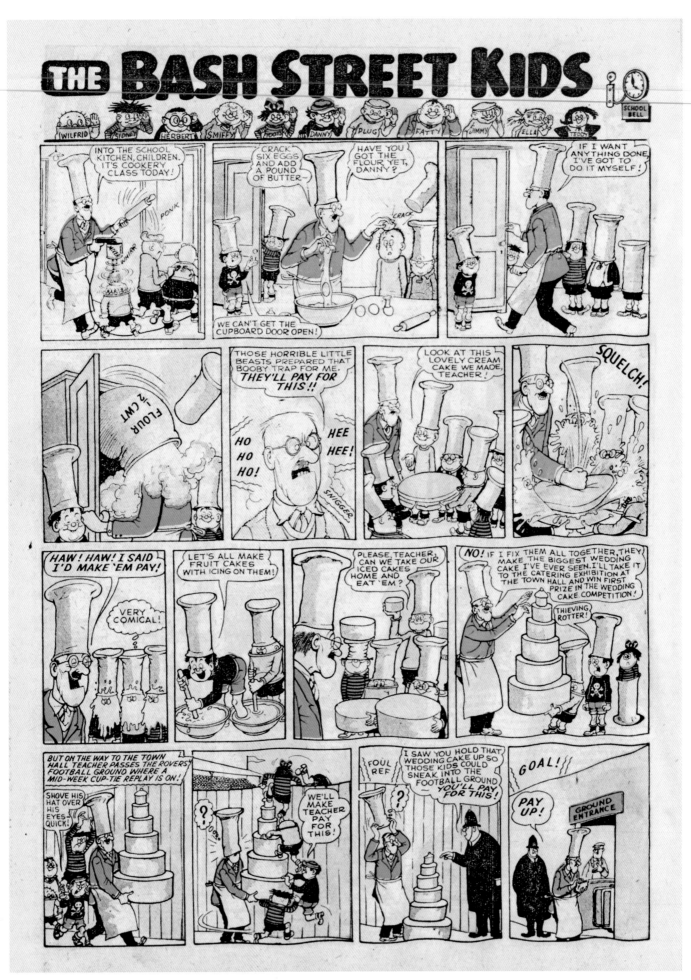

Cookery class has always been a recipe for chaos. Mischievous children in the kitchen was a dreaded thought for both pupils and teachers.

MR CREEP, the Third Form Master at Greytowers School, could never be sure what his boys were going to be up to next, for among his pupils were Winker Watson, the world's wiliest wangler, and the wangler's pal, Tim Trott. One thing Creepy did know for certain, however, was that all of them were always starving!

HANDS UP THE BOYS WHO WANT CHIPS FOR SUPPER TONIGHT?

YOU KNOW US, MR CREEP, SIR— WE ALL DO!

GOOD! THEN WATSON, TROTT AND YOU LOT GO ALONG TO THE KITCHEN WITH COOK.

The boys' teeth watered at the thought of the feast to come. They didn't know they'd been tricked.

In the kitchen, there was no sign of any chips. But there was a big bag of spuds, and loads of knives!

IT'S NOT MY FAULT, BOYS. MR CREEP SUGGESTED IT WHEN I TOLD HIM MY ELECTRIC PEELER WAS BROKEN!

POTATOE

POTATOE

However, Winker and Company didn't grumble too much, for they were peeling the spuds for themselves. The aroma of frying drifted over the school wall.

SNIFF-SNIFF! AAAH! DO YOU CHAPS SMELL WHAT I DO...?

Those bobbies were attending a police college next door to Greytowers, and they were hungry too. While some of them took up Cookie's attention, another grabbed several helpings of the chips!

The boys looked glum instead of happy at supper time. There were only a couple of measly mouthfuls on each plate!

COOK! WHY HAVE YOU ONLY GIVEN THE BOYS HALF A DOZEN CHIPS EACH FOR SUPPER?

DON'T BLAME ME MR CREEP. I FRIED EVERY POTATO THAT THEY PEELED.

Creepy took Cookie's word for it that the boys must have been slacking.

YOU LAZY LOT! IT'S POTATO PEELING FOR YOU AGAIN TOMORROW, AND DON'T ARGUE!

OH, SIR, IT'S NOT FAIR!

NEXT MORNING

Winker knew that bags of spuds had been peeled, and he was suspicious. He went snooping around and found a clue.

POLICE COLLEGE

JUST WHAT I THOUGHT I'D FIND! PIECES OF GREASY NEWSPAPER!

Come to the cookhouse door, boys—Scrape your dinner off the floor, boys!

Those sneaky bobbies had made a clever enemy! While the Third Formers peeled spuds, Winker whispered to Tim.

PSST, TROTTY! I'VE GOT A WHEEZE TO GET US OUT OF THIS JOB!

Cookie bustled about the kitchen, and as he passed, carrying a big bowl of gooey mixture, Winker shot out a foot.

Cookie's foot came down on those rolling potatoes—and Cookie and bowl went up in the air.

WHOOPS!

What goes up must come down—and Cookie did. So did his bowl. And while he was blinded with goo, Winker nipped off.

THAT WORKED, TROTTY, AND I'LL BE BACK IN A SECOND.

GROO! NOW HOW ON EARTH DID THAT HAPPEN?

Winker kept on running and dashed into the police college grounds. As he expected, he was stopped by a bunch of bobbies.

HOLD IT, SON! WHAT HAVE YOU BEEN UP TO?

Winker's answer, given in a frightened, out-of-breath voice, alarmed the bobbies.

NOTHING! IT'S COOK—HE'S HAD AN ACCIDENT IN THE KITCHEN!

OUT OF THE WAY, SON! WE'LL GO AND HELP HIM!

The bobbies dashed off, and Winker hugged himself. There would be another accident any minute now!

There was! And it was a beauty. Those rushing coppers went flying as they trod on the spilt potatoes.

WHOOPS!

That wasn't all that went flying either. As the four bobbies went crashing, they upset tables loaded with food Cookie had been preparing.

Cookie was wild when he saw the mess, and he complained to the Superintendent of the cop college.

I'VE TOLD MY MEN OFF FOR SPOILING THE DINNER YOU HAD PLANNED, COOK, AND THEY'RE TO HELP YOU GET ANOTHER READY. WHAT DO THE BOYS WANT THIS TIME?

CHIPS!

CHIPS!

What the boys wanted meant that the bobbies had a lot of work to do—peeling spuds. And it served them right.

HEY, TROTTY, LISTEN TO THIS . . . "THE POLICE FORCE WAS FORMED IN 1829 BY SIR ROBERT PEEL, AND BECAUSE OF THIS, FOR MANY YEARS THEY WERE KNOWN AS 'PEELERS'!"

Beano and Dandy characters are no strangers to disastrous diets. Over the years, they've come up with inventive ways to pass up the pastries and boycott the buns.

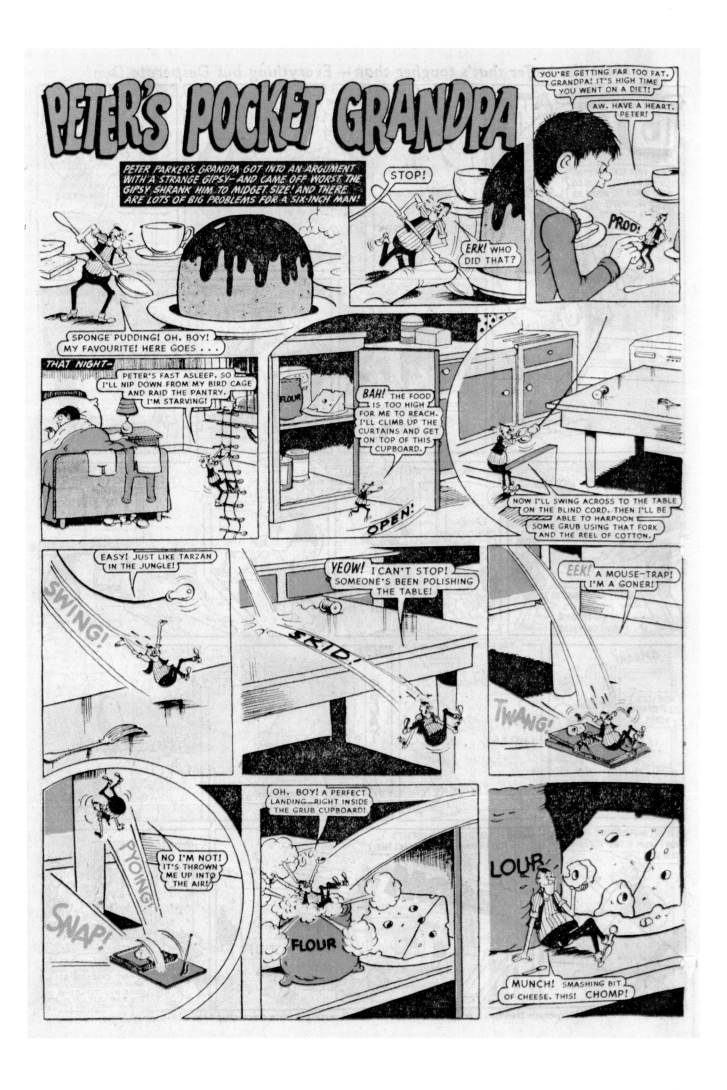

Even superheroes need to watch their waistline. Fed up of bananas, Eric finds they'll be all he can eat after scoffing his way past this crook's edible attacks.

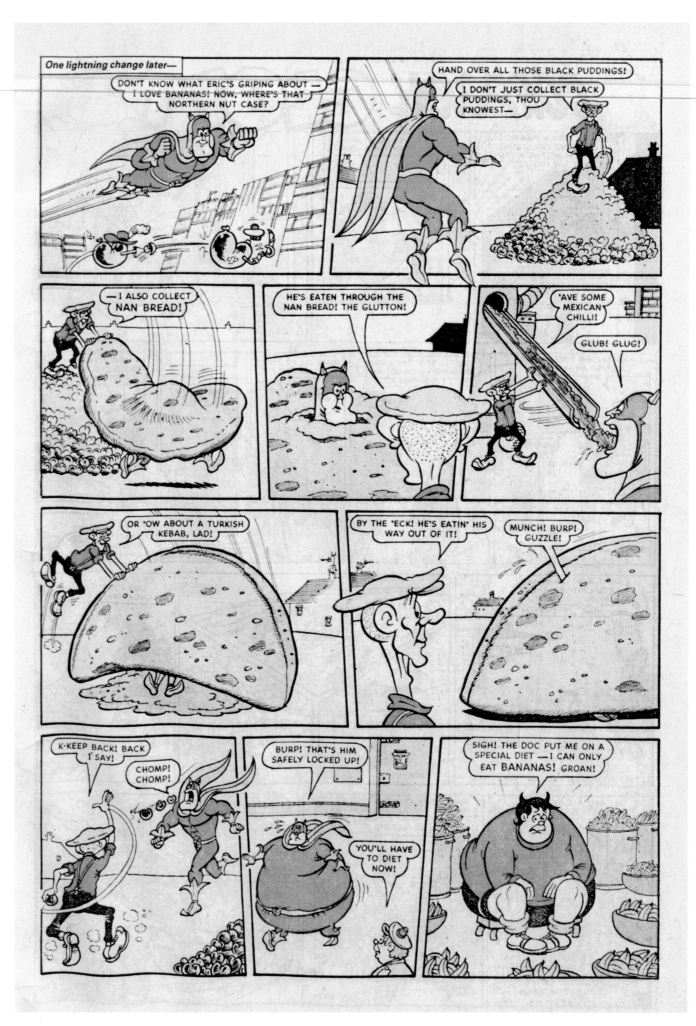

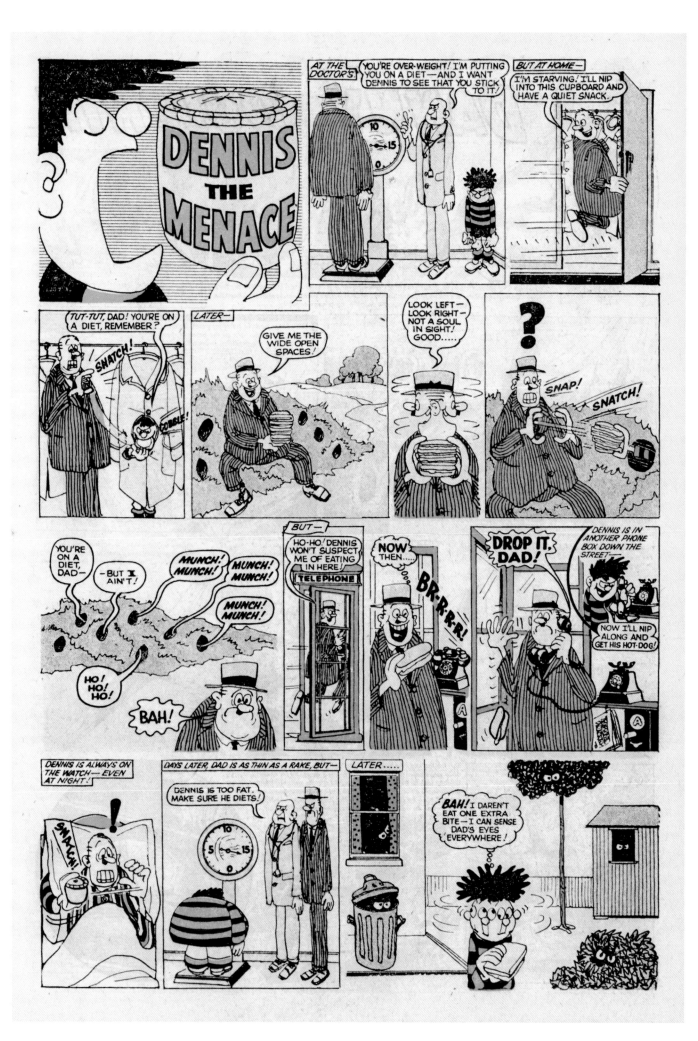

In these strips from 1977, Gnasher gnaws his way through huge feasts with a larger than life appetite.

Ingenious inventors saw food as a brilliant basis for new creations.

LORD SNOOTY

THREE BEARS

SOMEWHERE IN THE DESERT!

COO! THEY'RE GOING TO SEND A SPACEMAN UP TO THE MOON.

'CHOMPY FOOD SUPPLIES'

HANK

YOU'RE THE VERY MAN FOR THE FLIGHT, SHORTY. THE ROCKET CAN ONLY CARRY A VERY LIGHT MAN.

GOSH! THANKS, CAPTAIN!

MEANWHILE HANK HAS AN IDEA!

CACKLE! IF I CAN FOOL THE BEARS INTO ENTERING THAT ROCKET, THEY'LL END UP ON THE MOON! THAT'LL STOP THEM RAIDING MY FOOD-STORE.

WOW! LOOK AT THAT! LET'S GO, BEARS!

FREE FEED IN SKYSCRAPER! THIS WAY

THIS MUST BE THE PLACE!

FREE FEEDS

YIPPEE! GRUB—LOVELY GRUB!

MEANWHILE IN THE CONTROL ROOM—

SOUNDS LIKE SHORTY'S READY. PREPARE TO FIRE ROCKET!

CHOMP! CHOMP! CHOMP!

CURLY

THREE-TWO-ONE-ZERO!

STARTER BUTTON

JAB

ERK! THIS SKYSCRAPER'S MOVING!

WHOOOSH!

BUT IT DOESN'T MOVE VERY FAR BECAUSE THE FAT BEARS ARE TOO HEAVY FOR IT.

CRA-A-ASH!

HANK'S FOOD STORE

I DON'T KNOW WHAT'S HAPPENING, BUT HERE'S MORE GRUB SO WE WON'T ASK QUESTIONS! WE'LL JUST KEEP GUZZLING!

LATER

I CAN'T SEE THEM ON THE MOON, BUT I BET THEY'RE MISERABLE WHEREVER THEY ARE! SNIGGER!

HANK WILL BE MISERABLE WHEN HE FINDS OUT WHAT'S IN STORE FOR HIM.

Many of the characters were clueless when left to fend for themselves. Their creative cookery skills always led to laughter.

A tale that's sharp and full of bite — And ends with Creepy in a plight!

Winker's tricks are really smashers — To win the prize for the whitest gnashers.

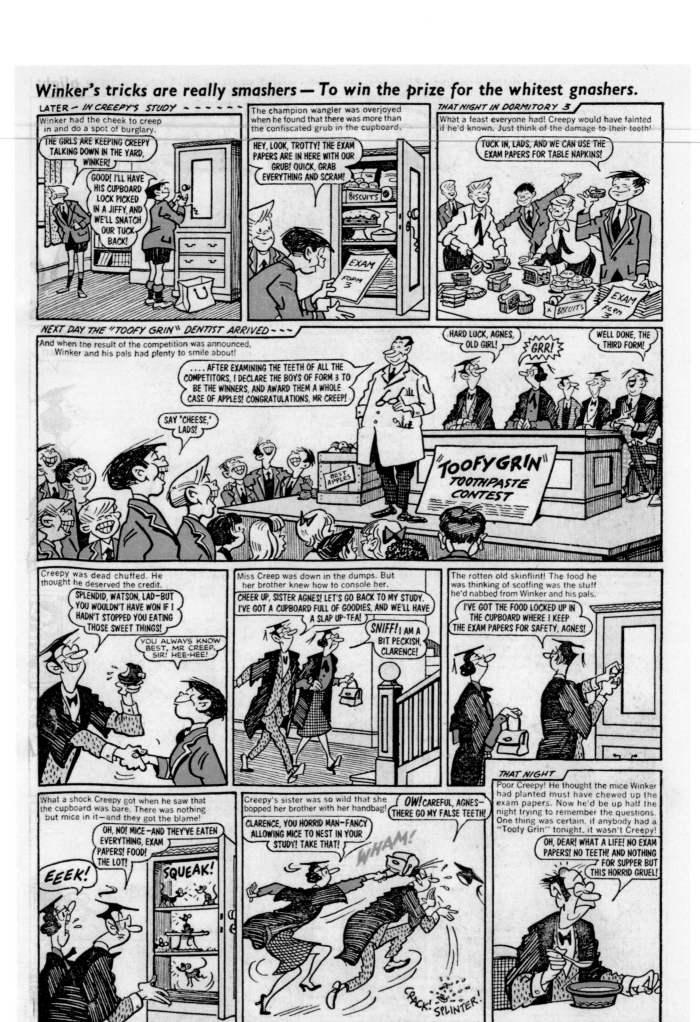

Beano's first cover star, Eggo, bit off more than he could chew in this comical contest.

PUNCH and JIMMY

It's mine!

BOP!

No, it's not. It's mine!

What are you two scrapping about now?

I want the last pie on the plate!

So do I!

Well, that's easily settled.

Bet she gives it to me.

No. She'll give it to me.

You're both wrong — CHOMP! — I'll eat it myself — GULP!

?

That's the end of that. I'll never buy another pie. They cause too much trouble.

But, Mum, we like pies!

I said, "No more pies." Out you go and play.

FURTHER DOWN THE STREET —

Ye Olde Pie Shoppe

YIPPEE! That's the very thing for us!

GRAND PIE-EATING CONTEST TODAY

We must enter for that!

LATER AT THE CONTEST —

GRAND PIE-EATING CONTEST

CHOMP! CHOMP!

SLURP! This is um plum pie.

SMACK!

MUNCH!

CHOMP! HEH! HEH! I'm beating you, pie-face.

GULP! Cheeky nit!

MUNCH!

SPLAT!

Who's a pie-face now?

THEN —

STOP THEM, SOMEBODY — GLURK!

Well, I won that fight.

We don't have time to argue! Here comes the Judge!

You've ruined the contest.

BACK HOME —

AGH! And I vowed I'd never buy another pie!

JUDGE

BILL 100 PIES AT 6ᵈ EACH £2·10/-

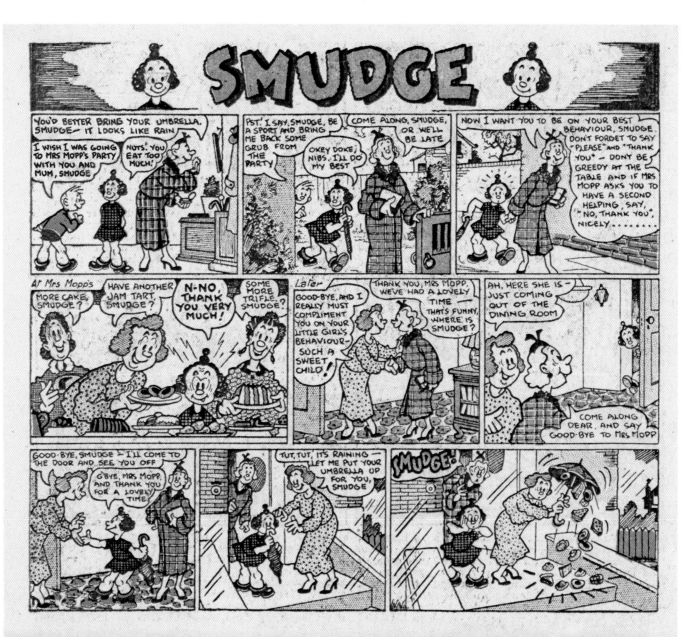

DOPEY DINAH—

Dinah's folk are wild because—She's steeped their duff in petrol sauce!

DOPEY DINAH

A rolling pin flies through the air—And shaves off most of Dinah's hair!

The apple doesn't fall far from the tree for many of our comic characters. Tempted by their mother's home baking, both Roger and Smasher work with their fathers to satisfy their sweet tooth.

The SMASHER

BOY, OH, BOY! CHERRY CAKE! SMASHING!

THAT CAKE ISN'T FOR YOU! SCRAM— OR I'LL TELL YOUR FATHER!

OOYAH!

SLAM!

WATCH ME CARRY THE TABLE AWAY ON MY BACK. SEE. I'M INVISIBLE!

LATER

CHATTER! CHATTER!

MUM AND HER FRIENDS ARE TOO BUSY GOSSIPING TO NOTICE ME! NOW'S MY CHANCE TO SNATCH THAT CAKE!

EEH! THIS HOUSE IS HAUNTED! THAT TABLE'S MOVING ON ITS OWN!

BUT MUM DOESN'T BELIEVE IN GHOSTS!

OUT YOU COME, YOU BRAT! I'M GOING TO LOCK YOU UP IN YOUR BEDROOM!

OUCH!

PET MOUSE

HA—HA! MUM FORGOT TO LOCK THE WINDOW!

THEN—

IN YOU GO, MOUSE, AND SCARE MUM AND HER FRIENDS OUT OF THE ROOM!

A MOUSE!

HELP!

EEK!

NOW THE COAST'S CLEAR FOR ME TO SNAFFLE THE CAKE!

BUT A CAT SCENTS THE MOUSE—

AND A DOG SPOTS THE CAT!

WOOF! WOOF!

BUT THE DOG FANCIES THE CAKE—

GET OFF, YOU BRUTE!

GRR! WILL THAT BRUTE NEVER GO AWAY?

IT DOES—AN HOUR LATER!

NOW I CAN SNEAK UP TO MY BEDROOM AND EAT THE CAKE IN PEACE!

GULP! HELLO, DAD!

MUM THOUGHT YOU WERE STILL LOCKED IN THE BEDROOM AND I GOT THE BLAME OF STEALING THAT CAKE!

SHE LOCKED ME IN HERE TOO, BUT I MANAGED TO SNEAK IN THESE COUPLE OF BOTTLES OF LEMONADE!

GOOD WORK, DAD! WE'LL SHARE! MUM BAKES A SMASHING CAKE!

The Three Bears

GUESS WHAT PA AND TEDDY ARE LOOKING AT, READERS?

THE ANSWER IS THAT MA HAS JUST BAKED A ROLY-POLY PUDDING.

CHOMP! I'M AFRAID THIS IS LAST OF THE GRUB, EXCEPT FOR THAT MOULDY OL' DUMPLIN'!

LATER!
M-M! A MONSTER ROLY-POLY PUD! WE'VE JUST GOTTA WIN THAT!

DODGE CITY TIMES
GREAT CROSSWORD PUZZLE COMPETITION
YOU CAN WIN THIS SUPER PRIZE
FIRST CORRECT ENTRY TO ARRIVE AT OUR OFFICE WINS

WE'LL GET AN ENTRY FORM RIGHT AWAY!

WHAT'S A SEVEN-LETTER WORD MEANING 'A HOT HILL'?
IT SAYS HERE, 'VOLCANO'!
CROSSWORD CONTEST

BUT—
COO! OUR ENTRY WILL NEVER GET TO DODGE CITY BEFORE THAT LOT, PA!

SO, IN THE PONY EXPRESS STABLE—
OH, BOY! FOOD!
PLOP!

AND WHEN THE PONY EXPRESS SETS OUT WITH ALL THE OTHER COMPETITION ENTRIES—
DODGE CITY
DOGGONE! WE'LL BE WEEKS GETTIN' THERE!
BUMP!

PA SETS OUT TO DELIVER HIS OWN ENTRY.
HMM, THE MEDICINE MAN IS SENDING HIS CROSSWORD ENTRY BY CARRIER VULTURE! I'LL HAVE TO PUT A STOP TO THAT!
WHEEZE!

SO TEDDY SENDS UP HAROLD, HIS PET HAWK!
STICK 'EM UP! THIS IS A HOLD-UP! GIMME THAT ENVELOPE!

A FEW DAYS LATER.
BEARS' CAVE
CONGRATULATIONS, BEARS! YOU'VE WON THE 'DODGE CITY TIMES' CROSSWORD CONTEST....
CROSSWORD CONTEST
RESULT:— WINNER:— PA BEAR

....IT GIVES ME GREAT PLEASURE TO PRESENT YOU WITH THIS BEAUTIFUL PERSIAN CARPET!
WHAT? WE THOUGHT THE PRIZE WAS A ROLY-POLY PUD!

BEARS' CAVE
CHOMP! MUNCH!
CRACK!
GOOD LUCK TO 'EM! I'VE WORN OUT TWO SETS OF TEETH ON THAT CARPET!
WELL, WE EITHER EAT THIS CARPET, OR WE STARVE!
MOANING MOTH

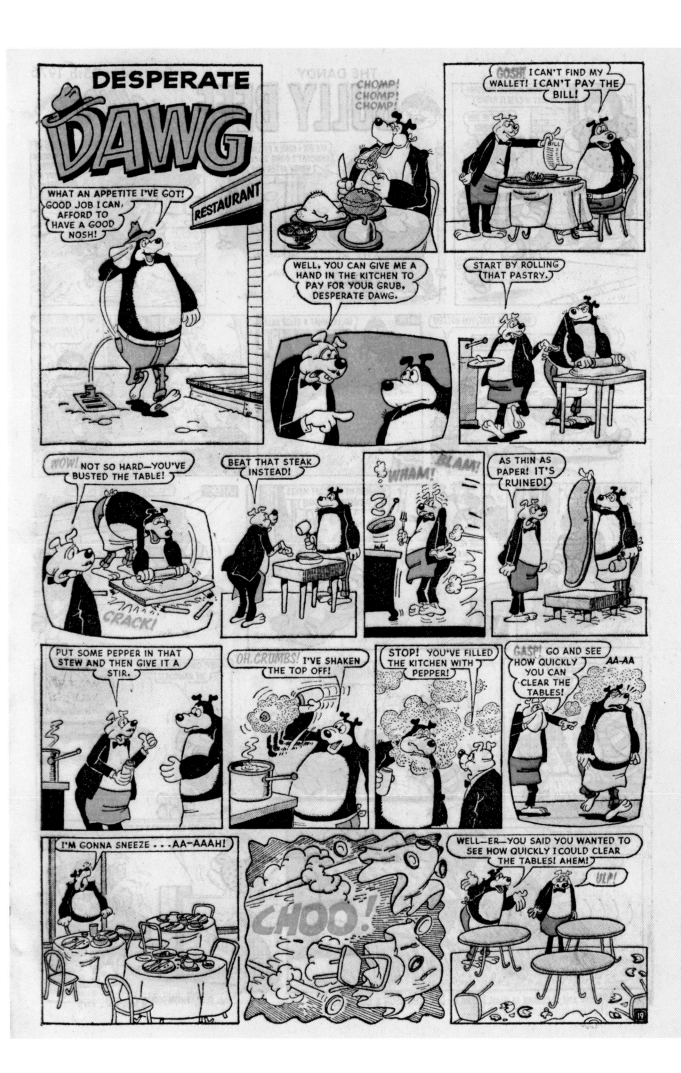

A trail of sticky fingers lands both Roger and Greedy Pigg in trouble in these two classic comic strips.

Coconut capers were a carnival favourite for some of these comic characters.

The Dandy

EVERY TUESDAY.

2p

NO. 1556
SEPT. 18th
1971.

THE TRICKS OF SCREWY DRIVER

The Dandy and Beano have served up a feast of fun for over eighty years, thanks to the comedic cast with a hunger for adventure. Their gut-busting antics have captured the hearts and imaginations of thousands of readers over the decades, expanding the appetite for classic British comics, with the characters continuing to entertain the young and young-at-heart today.

Food has fuelled much of the laughter in these comic strips. From World War Two to the present day, these characters have cooked up a chaotic storm in pursuit of their favourite dishes. These strips have shown the very best baking blunders, diet dodges and pantry pranks from DC Thomson's archives. The secret recipe to these comic capers is a heaped measure of laughter.

Which of our classic titles wins this ultimate Food Fight? That is for you to decide!

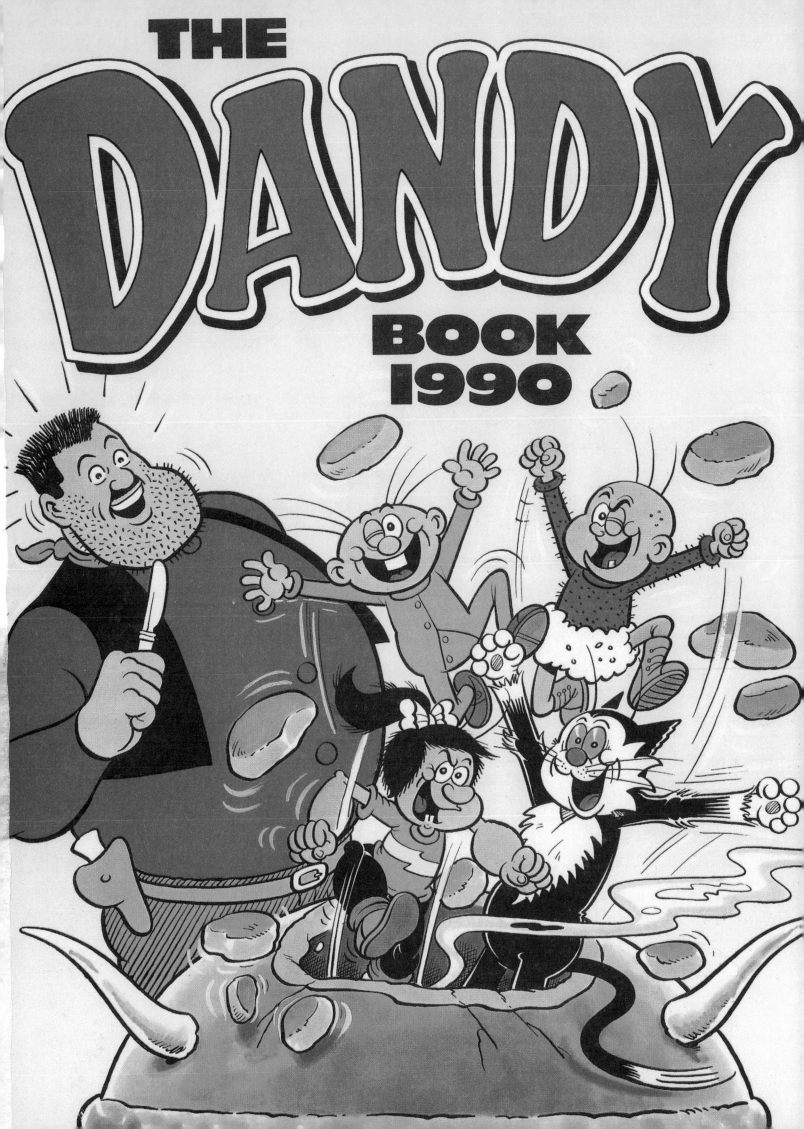

THIS STEAK IS TOUGH! I'M BENDING THE KNIVES AND FORKS AND~

~CUTTING UP THE PLATE~BUT NOT THE STEAK!

AARGH! HELP! MY SOUP IS EXPLODING ALL OVER THE KITCHEN!

WOW!

NEXT DAY

I HOPE THE RECIPE WAS RIGHT. THE CAKE SEEMS A BIT HEAVY!

RUMBLE

LOOK, BEEFY—THE GIRLS HAVE ARRANGED A SLAP-UP FEED IN THE RESTAURANT ACROSS THE STREET IF YOU'LL LET THEM HAVE THEIR MUMS' GRUB BACK!

ER-OKAY, CHIPS! TELL THEM TO HELP THEMSELVES!

TOLL GATE

BAKERY EXHIBITION FREE SAMPLES TO T... PUBL...

WAY IN

IDEA

EXHIBIT 5 APPLE PIE

REVENGE

AH, WELL! ONE LESS FOR DINNER—WHASSAT?

HUP!

HELP! THE SAUSAGES ARE BARKING!

YOW! THEY'RE ALIVE!

BOW-WOW

BOW-WOW

BOW-WOW

YOU ARE THE MESSIEST EATER I HAVE EVER SEEN!

@#!!☆&#!

BURP!

LATER—

WHAT WAS THAT YOU WERE SAYING ABOUT A DISGUSTING MESS, PA?

CAKE MIX

GOING TO MAKE A GINGERBREAD MAN, IVY?

NO, I'M GOING TO MAKE A GINGERBREAD...

STIR

Flour